FOLLOW THAT CHIMP

Philippe Dupasquier

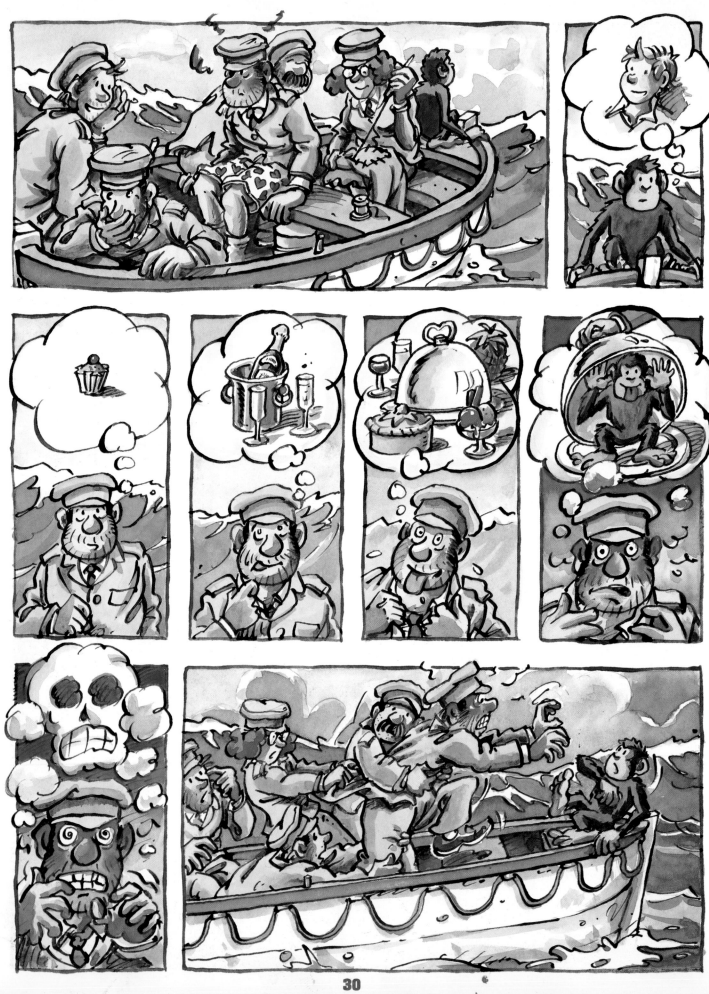

The End

First published 1992 in *Snap* magazine
This edition published 1993 by Walker Books Ltd
87 Vauxhall Walk, London SE11 5HJ

© 1992 Philippe Dupasquier

Printed and bound in Hong Kong by
South China Printing Co. (1988) Ltd

British Library Cataloguing in Publication Data
A catalogue record for this book is available
from the British Library.

ISBN 0-7445-2511-X

WALKER BOOKS
LONDON